LOVE, P.

by Gray Crosbie

2019

Wicked Wee Bk #2
by
Knight Errant Press

Published in 2019 by Knight Errant Press
Part of the Wicked Wee Bks series (#2)
Falkirk, Scotland

ISBN 978-1-9996713-4-1

Printed and bound by Mixam
Watford, Hertfordshire WD25 7GS
United Kingdom

Editor: N. Kunitsky

www.knighterrantpress.com

for May

CONTENTS

THE FIRST TIME

I don't remember my first kiss. I slept through it.

But he told me it was nice.

LOVE, PAN-FRIED

You always said I loved you too much, and I guess you were right. You said it again that day by the pond, when you told me how you weren't responsible for my happiness and your eyes matched the water, all sun-speckled and murky. That day when I loved you so hard that you exploded into a million pieces.

For the most part, you landed in the water. I jumped in after your scattered chunks but the fish gobbled you up; they consumed you so quickly, I guess they loved you too.

So I fished until it was dark, that day, that night, until I was sure I had caught every last one. Then I carried you home, nestled inside their stomachs.

They still fill my entire freezer, those fish. But if ever I feel sad, and sometimes I do, I fry one up. They make me feel better, I love them too much.

BIGFOOT'S TEA PARTY

The sun hadn't quite set but you'd trapped fireflies in jars to set the mood. I liked how you'd laced the trees with bunting made from shredded summer dresses. We sat on toadstool-cushioned tree stumps as you fed me nettle tea and mud cakes.

Then you sang, in howls and lonely whines. If you hadn't tied me up I would have held your hand.

AT SEA

The smell of piña coladas and perfumes not her own wash over me in waves, making me feel seasick. It's 4:32 a.m. as she clambers aboard our bed, throws her limbs across my body and clings on to me as though I'm a raft. As though if I held still, if I just kept quiet enough, I could keep us both afloat while she sleeps, breathing hurricanes into my ear.

WORD ART

To me you were the pre-set Fill Effect in Windows 97, which Microsoft Word called: "Horizon".

That endearingly revolting blade of steel blue

against lace white,

colliding with heroin brown.

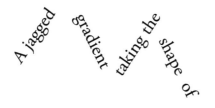

the word

N - O - R - M - A - L.

How you pressed yourself so tightly to the edges of those hollow letters.

INTIMACY, IN HD

If it wasn't for Clara I don't know how I'd survive. Just watching her do yoga or clean or nap, it calms me. With her sleepy breaths beside me at night I'm not alone, when it's impossible to switch off. I know lots of people prefer to watch Stan or Jennifer, but for me there is only Clara. I've been with her since she aired, since she was a child. She cried so much that first year. I know she doesn't know I'm watching, still I wonder—

Some days she doesn't move, just stares into the camera, right into me. I don't mind, but they flood her room, or send mosquitoes through the air vents when she sits too still or holds her breath for too long. They give her something to fight for, give us viewers something to root for.

Although once she didn't fight. They had to take her to the hospital. For a whole week I didn't have her, didn't know if she'd come back, didn't know how I'd manage to go on. My Tele-View flashed messages saying that I should tune into Jennifer, but instead I watched the live-cam of her empty room, I had to be there for her when she came back. But without her there all I saw was my reflection, my own TV-pale face and the people behind the cameras watching over my shoulder.

WINTER FRIENDS

The winter after you died it snowed too much. There was so much snow it stole my car and my cat and invaded the TV. It took everything that was left.

In the end, I built a snowman to survive. I made him look just like you, with your hat and the frown you wore when too cold.

And on the nights I couldn't sleep, I tiptoed down to the garden and pretended that I wasn't listening for the crunch of footsteps, any footsteps. I went to my snowman, whom I hugged and hugged until I couldn't feel him anymore and his smile melted down my pyjamas.

CITRUS FLAVOURED COPING
MECHANISMS

It
took me a while
to notice her scars. She
caught me fingering the ones
on her arm one morning. I
stared at the scattering of mela-
nin pips across her nose, avoid-
ing her eyes, and confessed
that I didn't understand.

And
she told me how
her scars don't have feeling, that they're her chewy-
tough pith. She told me how
she's all stringy numb and
manageable juicy seg-
ments. A tangerine.

TABOO

I hold his birth name in my mouth. It's weighted and tingles on my tongue. I flinch when he says mine, stabbing me somewhere between my heart and stomach. But it's wine coated, the corners of consonants rounded by his voice. I count down in my head: *three, two, one...*

"Susanne," I say.

And we cling together, squirming and giggling like school boys, experimenting with intimacy, testing boundaries.

ONE NIGHT WITH A WEREWOLF

I'm stepping into last night's jeans when she wakes. I try to pull them up before she notices the bite marks but I can see in her eyes that I'm not quick enough. She looks at the spattering of blood stains on my bedsheets, dry now, more brown than red.

"I'm so sorry," she says. "I've had such a crazy few weeks. I didn't realise it was that time of the month."

I shrug. "It's cool. It happens."

We smile at each other with our mouths but not our eyes. Her gaze flicks over the room, un-sure where to settle.

As I continue to dress she tucks her body into itself, folds her feet underneath her, digs elbows into ribs. She tugs at the sheet until it covers the thick fur that has sprouted from her arm-pits, legs and big toe. I pretend not to notice and rummage for a t-shirt.

"Sorry, I've got to get to work," I say. "You got someone to—"

"I'm fine."

We both look at what remains of her dress, red scraps like shredded meat on the floor. The pearls of her necklace are scattered around the room, tiny lost moons in the carpet. I grab some clothes, jeans and an old jumper from the dresser, and throw them too quickly onto the bed.

"Here, you can wear these."

"Thanks," she says, and rubs her thumb across a loose thread. "I'll bring them round sometime." "It's cool," I say, to the dark shadow above her lip. "Just keep them."

I leave the flat and walk as quickly as I can away from those soft howls leaping around the stairwell.

DISSECTION

You just sit there, an octopus preserved in your jar of formaldehyde secrets. Tentacles retracted, foetal, squirmed into yourself with a face so sapped of feeling I can't locate where your smile had once been. Yet still I want to smash the glass, spill you open and squish myself against you.

LINDA

I once loved a cactus girl who wore a ring of flowers around her head and used to hurt me when I got too close. I think she loved me too, in a way, though in the end it didn't work out.

It's been years now, and I know I should, but still I haven't teased her needles out from under my skin.

ASSESSMENT

I admit that I think that my labia are too large. Abnormally so. You decide to investigate.

I lie back on the bed as you angle the lamp. I feel the heat of its gaze on my inner thighs. You spread me open. Pinned under your fingers, displayed like butterfly wings, you study your specimen, saying nothing for far too long. While I lie still, playing dead.

THE KIND OF APPENDAGES LOST IN A BREAKUP

In the end I forgot to move out of her bathroom. I raked up the clothes and DVDs which I knew were mine (and some that weren't). But still my razor lies on the bath edge and in the blue jar with the sludge bottom my toothbrush stands, bristles nuzzled against hers.

I don't hope to get them back, only that her rebound girls look under the sink and find our Mooncups spooning.

I PAINT YOU IN BUBBLES

In the bath together, I paint you in bubbles. I craft bubble biceps, bubble forearms, bubble pecs. I ruffle on a soapy beard, but you look like Santa, it's too full, too fake. With a razor, still capped, I shave your cheeks, scrape and shape a face I think is manly. You smile and your moustache smudges against your nose.

When I reach for the cloud between your legs, you flinch, but don't stop me. We work together to shape genitals. You cup together balls of suds while I stroke a bubble patch into a shaft, round it, add girth. I trim the length, then you add on a bit extra. I circumcise you.

Complete, you shimmer, an illusion of handsome. We sit silent, the steady fizz of evaporating bubbles between us. I look away and pick at the ingrown hairs on my legs until the water turns cold.

When I turn back it's your familiar body again, shiny smears like scars where the bubbles had been. I meet your eyes, so determined and torn.

A final island of bubbles, the deflated remains of your penis, floats between us. I take a part of it and craft a plaster over the tiny puncture mark on your thigh, the first wound. I swear I can feel the throb of testosterone beneath my fingers. You take the last of the bubbles and, in gentle strokes, place a plaster over my racing heart.

CAVITIES

The creases in your teeth are packed with gnawed phonemes. I can only imagine how they must ache, filled with all the words you've chewed over and over but never said.

HAPPY VALENTINE'S DAY

He left on Valentine's Day, though not without a fight. He liked a fight. Especially the kind when the walls shook and I had to use my arms as shields.

I locked myself in the bathroom as soon as I could. I heard him storm around the hallway for a bit, shouting that this was it, and that he was never coming back. I crossed my fingers so tightly they hurt.

Then he slammed the door and everything was still. I sat for a bit, breathing, focussed on the ringing in my ears, rattling like the school bell at the end of playtime.

My stomach lurched. I flew over to the toilet and retched. And there, I came face to face with a tiny chunk of shit that he'd left, as though waiting for me at the bottom of the bowl, dark and shaped like a comma.

GRENADIER GIRLFRIEND

You pulled the pin, but I let go, so you say it was my fault that my heart exploded. All that was left of it were tattered ribbons, like ruby bunting, which, of course, I let you tie into bows through my ribcage.

MEMORIES IN A TEACUP

The teapot's lid jitters as she shuffles towards the table, her hand shaking under its weight. She pours the tea into my cup, an opaque stream of the deepest black, streaked with the colours of raw bruises. It glitters, like a liquid galaxy.

"Now remember," The Hag says, "she won't be real, only a memory."

I nod in response and reach for the cup. The steam smells like the underground, clean hair, snow–

"Oh!" she cries. I pause, bottom lip pressed to the warm china. She pushes a bowl towards me. "Perhaps some sugar, dear? Love can be quite bitter."

ATOMIC

Physicists say that touch is an illusion. No two atoms can ever actually meet, which means that nothing, in fact, touches anything else.

A fact I remind myself of when I imagine you kissing her. I try to remember that your lips couldn't possibly touch hers and anyway, you'd been honest. You'd said you were sorry.

But at 3 a.m., when you're sleeping, and I'm pressing my quantum-mechanical body into yours I swear I can feel all the repulsion of protons and attraction of electrons. And where my body meets your skin, I think I can feel that the science is right. I think I can feel, that we aren't actually touching.

LONG DISTANCE

On the outward journey, I met a technician. Together we discovered a moon completely carpeted with flowers, almost white, just the tiniest shade blue. Alice Blue, she called it.

She stayed there. She wouldn't come back, I couldn't stay. I don't see her now, but still I shoot message-bottles into space, in the hope that they reach my Alice Blue.

INSIDE WE'RE WILD THINGS

Inside we are all wild things. It hides deep, longing to prowl and roam and soar but instead that wild side is stuck clawing and gnashing at neatly ironed skin.

You're an owl, I know it. Sometimes it flits across your eyes and in the dark I feel the scrape of your talons, sharp enough to pierce soft sides. Burrowed in the duvet, I watch you perch on the open window, your nightdress moon-drenched, and wonder if you'll suddenly take flight. I fall asleep before you return, and in the morning, I can smell the rot of prey between your teeth.

But not all our wild things are owls or wolves or jaguars. Some of us are voles, hares, even door mice, whose whiskers twitch when they hear you coming.

31

THE REMARKABLE GIRLS YOU CAN FIND IN THE PECULIAR DEPTHS OF THE INTERNET

All her online photos had been of her cats so I wasn't prepared for the blue hair or the fact that I'd find her septum piercing adorable.

We chatted, words flowed. She told me about her art studio, about backpacking around South America, about the notebook in which she collected the stickers you get on bananas. I felt compelled to tell her secrets but instead talked about my work, my migraines, my mother.

Eventually the words began to ebb away and we sipped at dregs of coffee.

She smiled.

"Want to see something?" she asked.

Before I could answer she leaned forward and brought her hands together on the table, palms up. I watched, waited. Then her hands started to glow. I jumped when the first spark of light burst out. Suddenly dozens of tiny fireworks shot between her palms and erupted like shattered rainbows, while doll-sized rockets looped and boomed around her fingers. I watched, unblinking, until the show ended and she blew away the twirls of smoke and ember wisps. She stood.

"I'm sorry, I've got somewhere to be. It was nice to meet you."

She dropped money for her coffee on the table, the exact amount in change. By the time I found words to say goodbye, she was gone.

I sat with the space in her chair and the smell of burnt wood. No one seemed to notice, the world rolled on, but for a moment I couldn't quite see for the inky splodges in my eyes, the afterimage of colour.

LOVE CHARM

She said she loved the freckle in my philtrum. The adorable quirk the rest of me could never live up to.

20P

Another twenty pence piece clunks to the bottom of the payphone, even though we haven't spoken through the last £1.40. I drag my nail along the ridged cord in time with the sound of her breathing. My own breath fogs on the receiver. The button in the cradle clicks gently as I stroke it.

The booth smells like damp pennies and piss. Scattered around the phone are strip-club business cards. The walls are vandalised with proclamations of love and disproportioned penises. I read a message, carved in the jagged scratches left in the plastic wall: don't forget to say I love you.

My mouth opens itself, as if to say something, as she hangs up.

DREAMING GROWN-UP DREAMS

I know a woman who sleeps with a unicorn tucked under her arm because it's stuffed with the kind of security that people just aren't.

FAIRY TALE ENDINGS

I'm alone again. It's late but I've found a club, followed the neon glow to the end of an alley where the words "Happy Ever After" float above an entrance with no bouncer.

Inside it's busy. I'm looking around for my friends when a bar girl asks what I want. I grab a drinks menu but it's all fuzzy-jumbled, so I point at random instead.

"Frog Sparkle?" she says and looks at me funny. "Do you want the kiss with it?"

"Yeah, of course," I reply, winking, like I order it all the time.

I'm smiling at these girls next to me who're smiling back when the bar girl slides my drink towards me. It's huge and colourful, as though there's a melted down circus inside and tastes just as good. It tastes so good that I chug it down, I just can't stop.

It isn't until it's nearly finished that I see the frog, limp heavy, sliding face first down the inside of the glass towards me.

I just manage to close my mouth in time and its lips all cold and slick-firm collide with my own.

I drop the glass. As it hits the ground it explodes, not just the glass but as though there were fireworks inside and for a second I see the frog amongst it all before it explodes too; then, suddenly, there's this naked guy, lying face down in all the bits of glass and spilled drink.

I'm scouring my lips with my sleeve and dancing around screaming – what the fuck what the fuck – as the bar girl rushes around. The smiling girls are gone.

"Sorry, that happens sometimes," the bar girl says, and drags the lifeless man by the leg from the dance floor. And I'm alone again, before I think to ask if I could just keep him.

HEART DECAY

We met on the anniversary of our breakup. We had a picnic in the walled garden of the derelict mansion once owned by people whose names we'd forgotten but remembered they were rich in the money kind of way. Sitting on a tartan raft in a sea of grassy neglect we drank from carefully mismatched cups and saucers. You scraped mould from the crust of a sandwich you'd made, gave me half.

When the sky ruptured into thunder and rain we folded our picnic into a sack and ran to the mansion, clambered in through the kitchen window. Inside we played house, threw china at each other with non-committal aim. With the shattered pieces we tried to make a mosaic of the story of our relationship, told in a mess of ceramic shards glued together with sugary tea.

On the second floor we found the master

bedroom, but chose a box room. We laid down the picnic blanket, then our wet clothes, then our skin and bones and burrowed into the deepest corners of each other; playing make-believe, pretending that love could put broken things back together.

SEMI-SKIMMED

I drank a carton of words for breakfast. I thought it would improve my vocabulary and I'd finally be able to string my emotions into sentences. Since in the last three months I've said "I'm fine" 132 times.

But the words curdled with the feelings in my stomach, and instead I spent the morning vomiting love poetry down the toilet.

LIVING WITH AN EX WHO ISN'T YOURS

My flatmate says she doesn't miss any of the girlfriends who've left in the last few months, and that she doesn't need any more. I keep telling her that I believe her.

Though through the wall I can hear that she now sleeps with the radio on, tuned to an uninhabited frequency. I lie in bed and imagine snowy static falling into all the quiet corners of her room.

And I've noticed that she's turned the temperature of the radiator in the bathroom up and the toilet roll now sits on top of it, where it's heated to exactly 34º C – the temperature of skin.

PREVIOUSLY PUBLISHED

The First Time, published in print by Bitterzoet Press, 2018.

Love, Pan-Fried, published online by Cease, Cows, 2017.

Big Foot's Tea Party, first published online by Leopard Skin and Limes, 2016; published in print by Dark Lane Books, in 'Dark Lane Anthology Vol. 3', 2016.

At Sea, first published by York-Juba Anthology, 2018.

One Night with a Werewolf, published in print by Freak Circus, in 'Freak Circus – Shame Issue', 2016.

Linda, published in print by Bitterzoet Press, 2018.

The Kind of Appendages Lost in a Break Up, published by Lighthouse Magazine, in the 'Queer' issue, 2017.

I Paint You in Bubbles, published online by Gender Trash Café, 2017.

Memories in a Teacup, published in print by Three Drops Press, in the 'Full Moon and Foxglove Anthology', 2016.

Long Distance, published as "Long Distance Love" by Blink Ink, in the 'Space' themed issue, 2017.

The Remarkable Girls You Can Find in the Peculiar Depths of the Internet, published online and in print by Litro, the 'Dating' issue, 2017.

Living with an Ex Who isn't Yours, first published as an ebook by Popshot, in the 'Romance' issue, 2018. Later published in print by Bitterzoet Press, 2018.

ABOUT THE AUTHOR

Gray Crosbie is a queer writer and spoken-word poet. Their writing often explores themes such as queerness, gender and mental health, and has been published in a wide range of anthologies and journals throughout the UK and as poetry films on BBC The Social. They perform regularly at literary events and cabaret nights around Scotland, with their full-length spoken-word show AMPHIBIOUS premiering at the Edinburgh Fringe in 2019. They live in Glasgow with their soon-to-be wife and their rescue dog Rooney. Find them in the book of faces at www.facebook.com/plantpoweredpoet.

ABOUT THE ILLUSTRATORS

Johanne Licard is a french, self-taught illustrator with a background in film-making. From growing up in the rapeseed fields of the outskirts of Paris, she's developed a taste for nature landscapes and motifs. She likes to focus on the feminine experience and draws diverse, true-to-life characters in scenes infused with a sensual and dreamy twist. A vintage design lover, she grabs her textures and color palettes from the 1960's and 1970's. She works for press, advertising and design companies and can be contacted at licard.johanne@gmail.com; her work can be seen at www.johannelicard.com.

Murphy Winter is a dark-humored werewolf enthusiast with a normal day job as a cover. Outside of work, he moonlights as a monster artist and is working towards freelancing full time in the future. He is passionate about fitness, dabbling in both circus and pole, lives part-time at the local gym and still finds time to eat far too much chocolate. His best buddy is his rescue dog Luca who has the pointiest feet of any dog in existence.

ABOUT THE PUBLISHER

Knight Errant Press publish queer stories from Scotland and beyond. Their recent publications have tackled queer topics such as gender, geography and contemporary local history. They publish inclusive books for readers from all walks of life, and at the heart of their work is the goal to shed light on experiences, stories and ideas that have been historically marginalised in mainstream publishing.

This book is **#2** in their **Wicked Wee Bks** imprint, which is all about tiny, beautiful books with a great impact.